Based on the best-selling keyboard method *by Kenneth Baker*

THE COMPLETE KEYBOARD PLAYER

Christmas Favourites

Wise Publications
part of The Music Sales Group
London/New York/Paris/Sydney/Copenhagen/Berlin/Madrid/Tokyo

Published by
Wise Publications
8/9 Frith Street, London W1D 3JB, UK

Exclusive Distributors:
Music Sales Limited
8/9 Frith Street, London W1D 3JB, UK.
Music Sales Pty Limited
120 Rothschild Avenue, Rosebery, NSW 2018, Australia.

This book © Copyright 2005 Wise Publications,
a division of Music Sales Limited.
Order No. AM983444
ISBN 1-84609-181-0

Compiled by Nick Crispin.
Music arranged by Paul Honey.
Music processed by Paul Ewers Music Design.
Cover photograph courtesy of Stockbyte.
Printed in the United Kingdom by
Printwise (Haverhill) Limited, Haverhill, Suffolk.

Your Guarantee of Quality
As publishers, we strive to produce every book
to the highest commercial standards.
This book has been carefully designed to minimise awkward
page turns and to make playing from it a real pleasure.
Particular care has been given to specifying acid-free, neutral-sized paper
made from pulps which have not been elemental chlorine bleached.
This pulp is from farmed sustainable forests and was produced with special
regard for the environment. Throughout, the printing and binding have been
planned to ensure a sturdy, attractive publication which should give years of enjoyment.
If your copy fails to meet our high standards, please inform us and
we will gladly replace it.

www.musicsales.com

Master Chord Chart

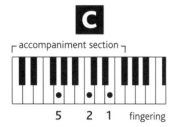

C
accompaniment section

5   2   1   fingering

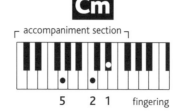

Cm
accompaniment section

5   2   1   fingering

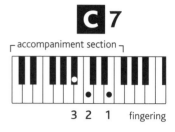

C7
accompaniment section

3   2   1   fingering

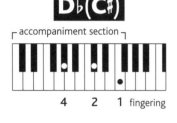

Db(C#)
accompaniment section

4   2   1   fingering

Db(C#)m
accompaniment section

4   2   1   fingering

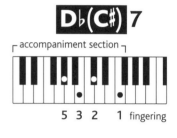

Db(C#)7
accompaniment section

5   3   2   1   fingering

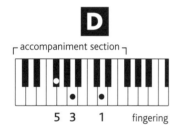

D
accompaniment section

5   3   1   fingering

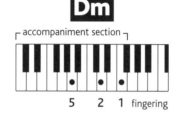

Dm
accompaniment section

5   2   1   fingering

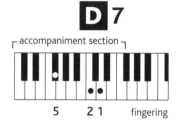

D7
accompaniment section

5   2 1   fingering

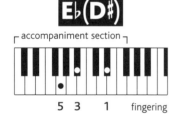

Eb(D#)
accompaniment section

5   3   1   fingering

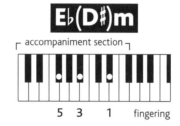

Eb(D#)m
accompaniment section

5   3   1   fingering

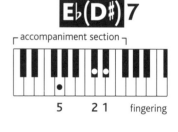

Eb(D#)7
accompaniment section

5   2 1   fingering

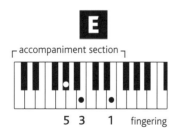

E
accompaniment section

5   3   1   fingering

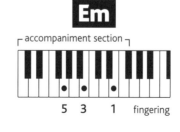

Em
accompaniment section

5   3   1   fingering

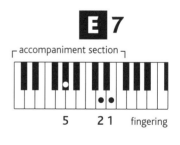

E7
accompaniment section

5   2 1   fingering

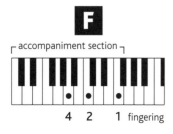

F
accompaniment section

4   2   1   fingering

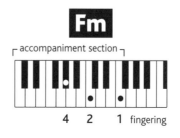

Fm
accompaniment section

4   2   1   fingering

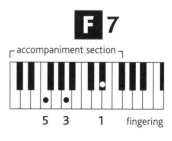

F7
accompaniment section

5   3   1   fingering

Master Chord Chart

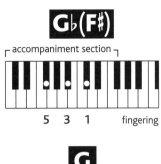

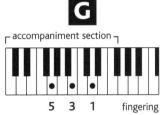

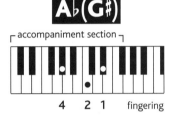

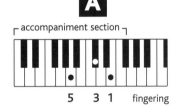

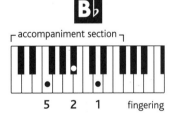

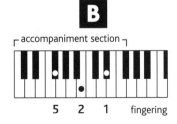

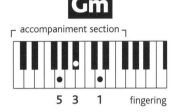

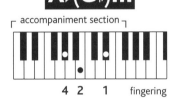

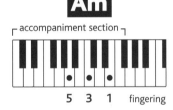

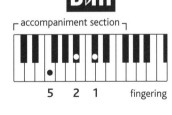

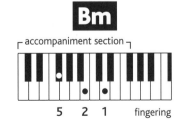

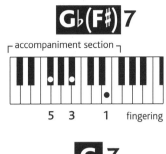

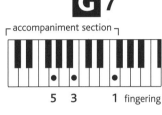

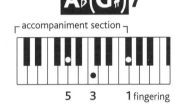

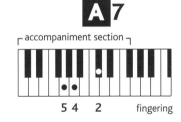

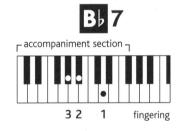

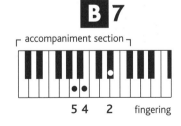

Extra chords used in this book:

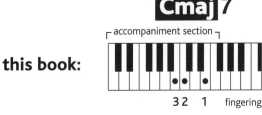

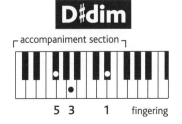

5

All I Want For Christmas Is You

Mariah Carey

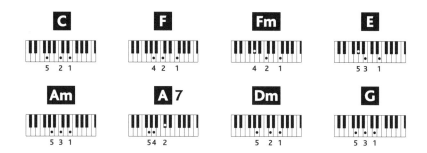

Voice: **Piano**
Rhythm: **Shuffle**
Synchro start: **On**
Tempo: **Bright shuffle** ♩ = 140

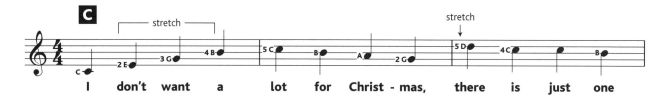

I don't want a lot for Christ - mas, there is just one

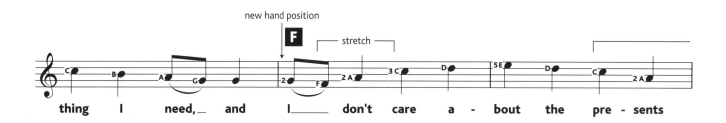

thing I need, ___ and I ___ don't care a - bout the pre - sents

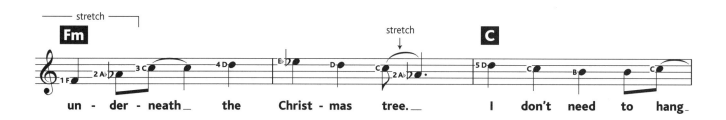

un - der - neath ___ the Christ - mas tree. ___ I don't need to hang ___

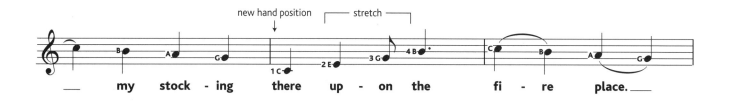

___ my stock - ing there up - on the fi - re place. ___

Words & Music by Mariah Carey & Walter Afanasieff

6

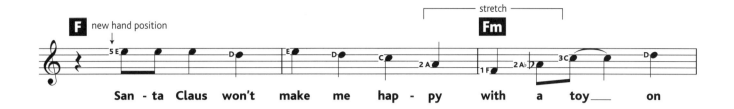

San - ta Claus won't make me hap - py with a toy___ on

Christ - mas Day.___ I just want you for my own,

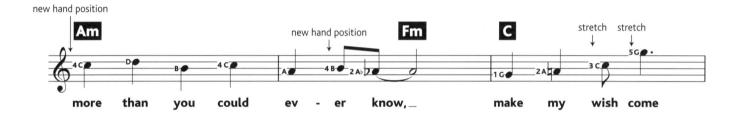

more than you could ev - er know,___ make my wish come

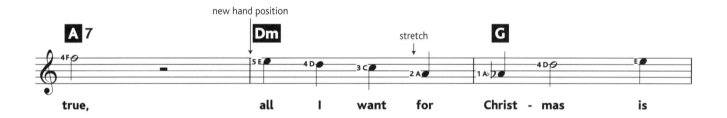

true, all I want for Christ - mas is

you._____ All I want for

Christ - mas is you._____

7

Away In A Manger

Traditional

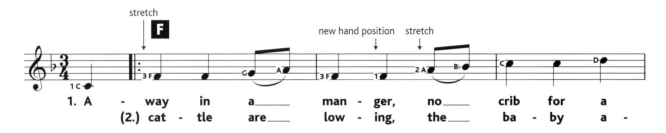

Voice: **Clarinet**
Rhythm: **Waltz**
Tempo: **Slowly** ♩ = 82

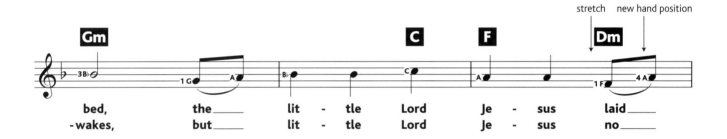

1. A - way in a_____ man - ger, no_____ crib for a
(2.) cat - tle are_____ low - ing, the_____ ba - by a -

bed, the_____ lit - tle Lord Je - sus laid_____
-wakes, but_____ lit - tle Lord Je - sus no_____

down his sweet head. The stars in the_____
cry - ing he makes. I love thee, Lord_____

bright sky looked_____ down where he lay, the_____
Je - sus, look_____ down from the sky and_____

Words: Traditional
Music by William Kirkpatrick

8

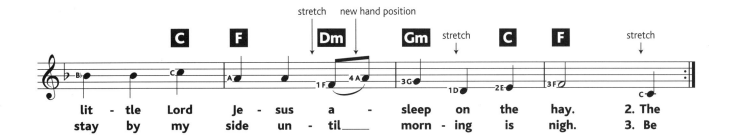

lit - tle Lord Je - sus a - sleep on the hay. 2. The
stay by my side un - til morn - ing is nigh. 3. Be

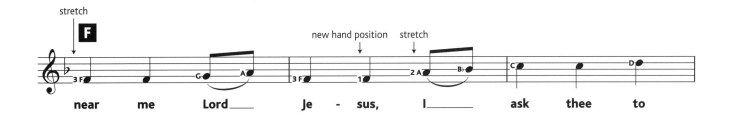

near me Lord Je - sus, I ask thee to

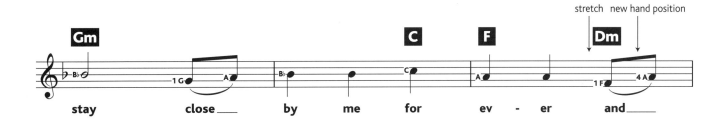

stay close by me for ev - er and

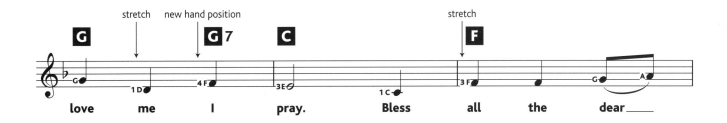

love me I pray. Bless all the dear

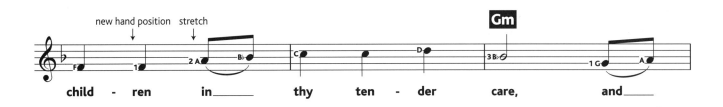

child - ren in thy ten - der care, and

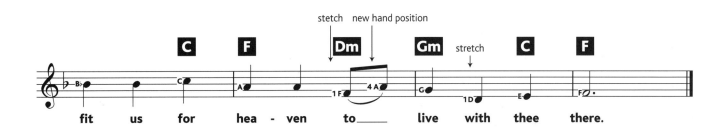

fit us for hea - ven to live with thee there.

Blue Christmas

Elvis Presley

Voice: **Guitar**
Rhythm: **Country**
Tempo: **Moderately** ♩ = 110
Synchro start: **On**

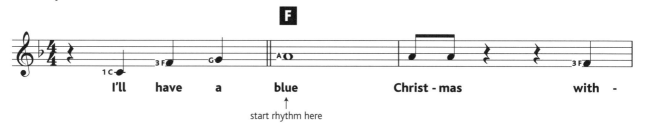

start rhythm here

I'll have a blue Christ - mas with -

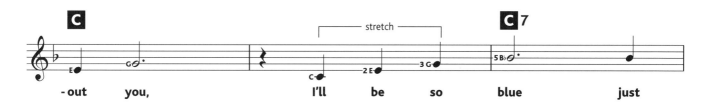

stretch

- out you, I'll be so blue just

new hand position

think - ing a - a - a - bout you. De - co -

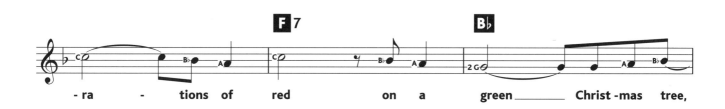

- ra - tions of red on a green _____ Christ - mas tree,

new hand position

won't be the same, dear, if

Words & Music by Billy Hayes & Jay Johnson

you're   not   here   with   me.   And   when   the   blue

snow-flakes   are   fall - ing,   that's   when   those

blue   mem - 'ries   start   call - ing.

new hand position

You'll be   do - in' al - right   with your   Christ - mas of

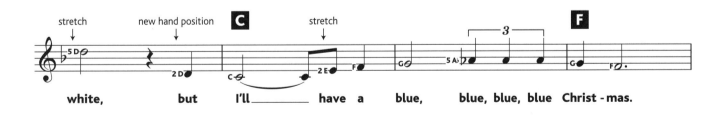

stretch   new hand position   stretch   3

white,   but   I'll_____ have   a   blue,   blue, blue, blue Christ - mas.

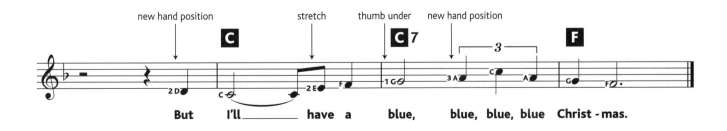

new hand position   stretch   thumb under   new hand position   3

But   I'll_____ have   a   blue,   blue, blue, blue Christ - mas.

Ding Dong! Merrily On High

Traditional

Voice: **Flute**
Rhythm: **Rock**
Synchro start: **On**
Tempo: **Quite fast** ♩ = 140

1. Ding   dong!   Mer - ri - ly   on   high,   in
2. E'en   so   here   be - low,   be - low   let

heav'n   the   bells   are   ring - ing.   Dong   dong!   Ve - ri - ly   the
steep - le   bells   be   swung - en.   And   'I - o,   i - o,   i-

sky   is   riv'n   with   an - gels   sing - ing.
-o'   by   priest   and   peo - ple   sung - en.

new hand position   new hand position

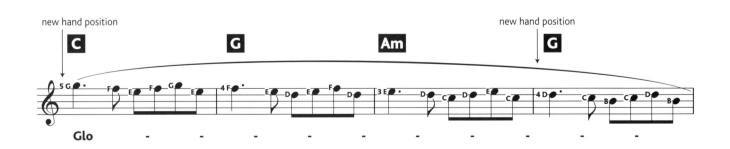

Glo -

Words by George Woodward
Music: Traditional

- - - - ri - a, ho - san - na in ex - cel - sis.

Glo - - - - - - - - - - - - -

- - - - ri - a, ho - san - na in ex - cel - sis.

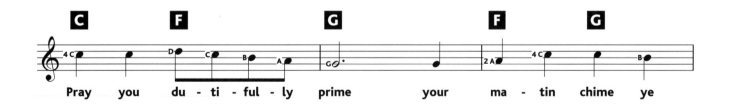

Pray you du - ti - ful - ly prime your ma - tin chime ye

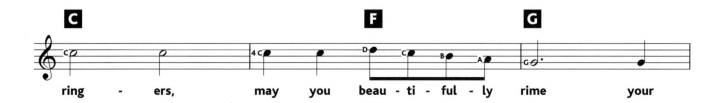

ring - ers, may you beau - ti - ful - ly rime your

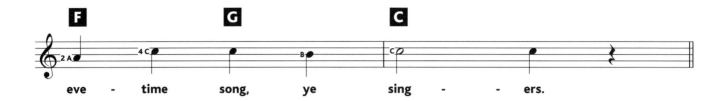

eve - time song, ye sing - - ers.

Glo - - - - - - - -

- - - - ri - a, ho - san - na in ex - cel - sis.

Glo - - - - - - - -

- - - - ri - a, ho - san - na in ex - cel - sis.

God Rest You Merry, Gentlemen

Traditional

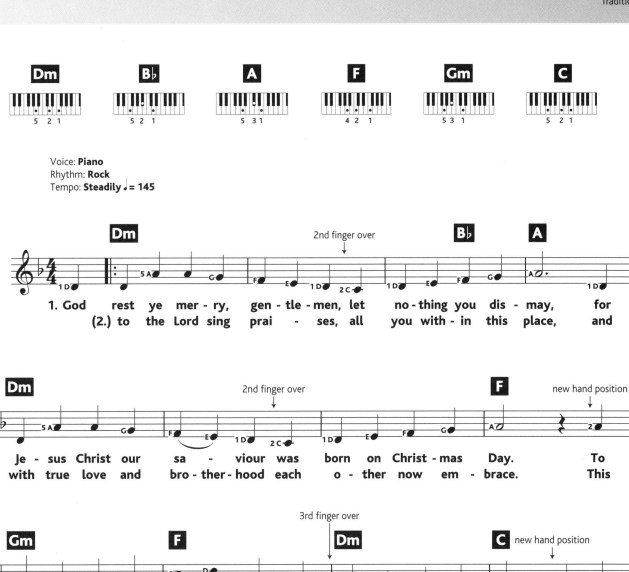

Voice: **Piano**
Rhythm: **Rock**
Tempo: **Steadily** ♩ = 145

1. God rest ye mer - ry, gen - tle - men, let no - thing you dis - may, for
(2.) to the Lord sing prai - ses, all you with - in this place, and

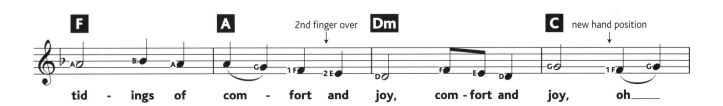

Je - sus Christ our sa - viour was born on Christ - mas Day. To
with true love and bro - ther - hood each o - ther now em - brace. This

save us all from Sa - tan's power when we were gone as - tray. ⎫
ho - ly tide of Christ - mas all o - ther doth de - face. ⎭ Oh___

tid - ings of com - fort and joy, com - fort and joy, oh___

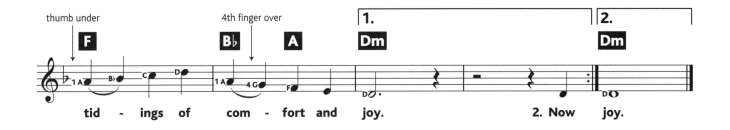

tid - ings of com - fort and joy. 2. Now joy.

Traditional

15

Hark! The Herald Angels Sing

Traditional

Voice: **Church organ**
Rhythm: **Rock**
Synchro start: **On**
Tempo: **Steadily** ♩ = 106

1. Hark! The he - rald an - gels sing___ glo - ry to the new born king.
2. Christ by high - est heav'n a - dored,___ Christ the ev - er - last - ing Lord.

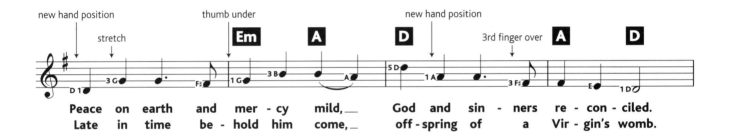

Peace on earth and mer - cy mild,___ God and sin - ners re - con - ciled.
Late in time be - hold him come,___ off - spring of a Vir - gin's womb.

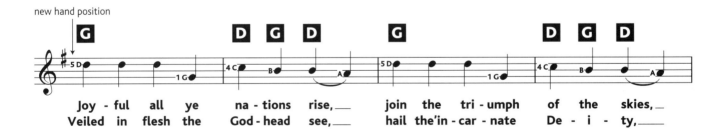

Joy - ful all ye na - tions rise,___ join the tri - umph of the skies,___
Veiled in flesh the God - head see,___ hail the'in - car - nate De - i - ty,___

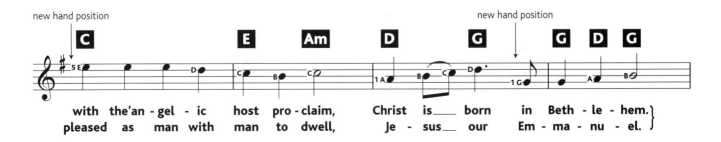

with the'an - gel - ic host pro - claim, Christ is___ born in Beth - le - hem.)
pleased as man with man to dwell, Je - sus___ our Em - ma - nu - el.)

Words by Charles Wesley
Music by Felix Mendelssohn

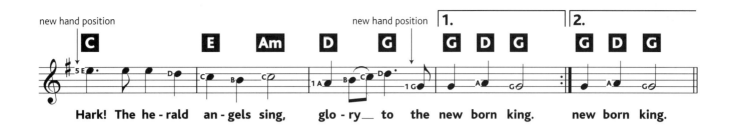

Hark! The he - rald an - gels sing, glo - ry __ to the new born king. new born king.

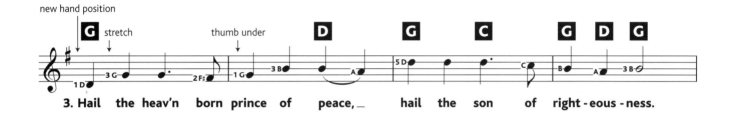

3. Hail the heav'n born prince of peace, __ hail the son of right - eous - ness.

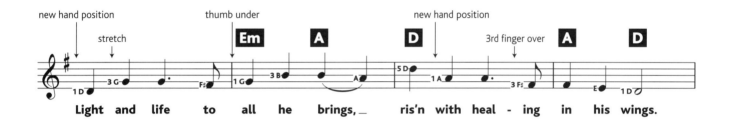

Light and life to all he brings, __ ris'n with heal - ing in his wings.

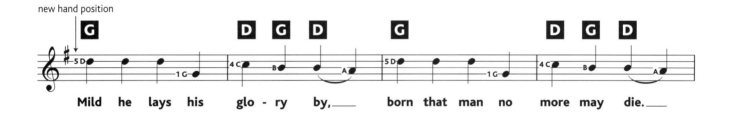

Mild he lays his glo - ry by, __ born that man no more may die. __

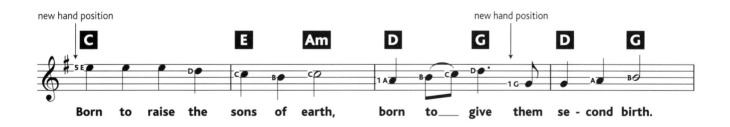

Born to raise the sons of earth, born to __ give them se - cond birth.

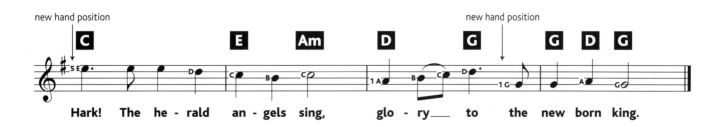

Hark! The he - rald an - gels sing, glo - ry __ to the new born king.

I Saw Mommy Kissing Santa Claus

Beverley Sisters

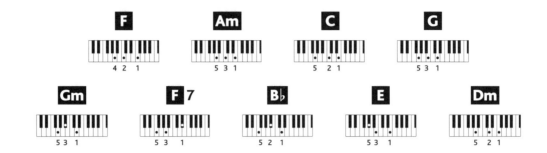

Voice: **Clarinet**
Rhythm: **Swing**
Synchro start: **On**
Tempo: **Moderately** ♩ = 124

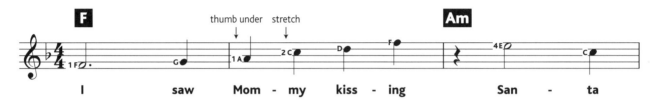

I saw Mom - my kiss - ing San - ta

Claus un - der - neath the mis - tle - toe last

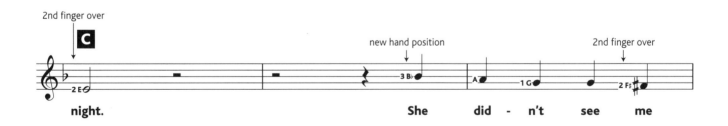

night. She did - n't see me

creep down the stairs to have a peep. She

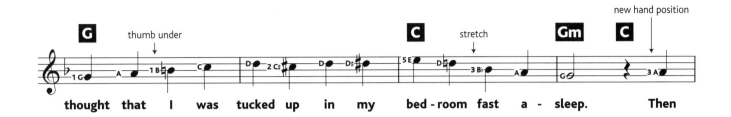

thought that I was tucked up in my bed-room fast a-sleep. Then

I saw Mom-my tick-le San - ta Claus

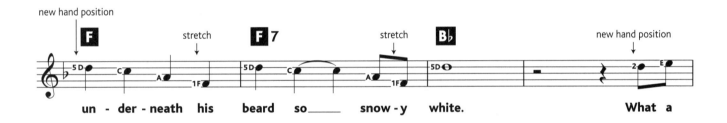

un - der-neath his beard so_____ snow-y white. What a

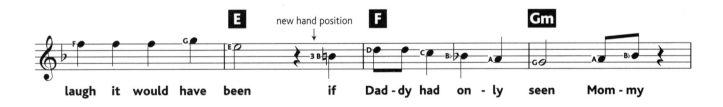

laugh it would have been if Dad-dy had on - ly seen Mom-my

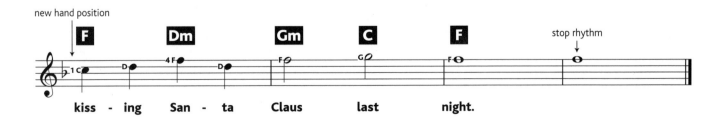

kiss - ing San - ta Claus last night.

Let It Snow! Let It Snow! Let It Snow!

Doris Day

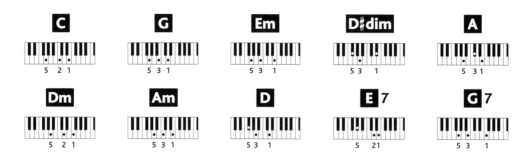

Voice: **Flute**
Rhythm: **Swing**
Tempo: **Moderate swing** ♩ = 106 (swung quavers)

Oh the wea-ther out-side is fright-ful, but the fire is so de-

-light-ful. And since we've no place to go, let it

snow, let it snow, let it snow. It does-n't show signs of

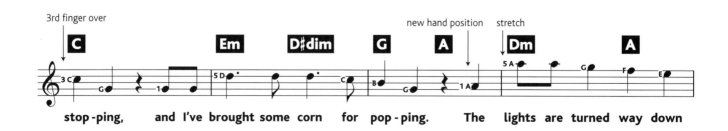

stop-ping, and I've brought some corn for pop-ping. The lights are turned way down

Words by Sammy Cahn
Music by Jule Styne
© Copyright 1945 Cahn Music Company, USA.
Warner/Chappell Music Limited.
All Rights Reserved. International Copyright Secured.

low,   let   it   snow,   let   it   snow,   let   it   snow.   When we

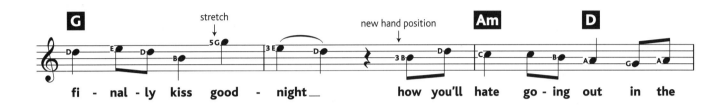

fi - nal - ly kiss good - night   how you'll hate go - ing out   in the

storm.   But   if   you   real - ly hold   me   tight,____

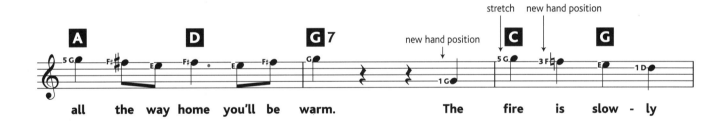

all   the way home you'll be warm.   The   fire   is   slow - ly

dy - ing,   and   dear,   we're still good - bye - ing.   But as

long as you love me so,   let it snow, let it snow, let it   snow.

Mistletoe And Wine

Cliff Richard

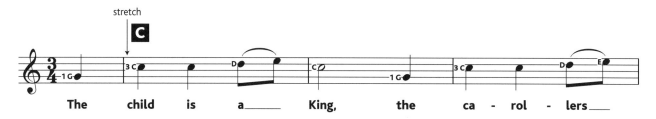

Voice: **Flute**
Rhythm: **Waltz**
Tempo: **Steadily** ♩ = 112

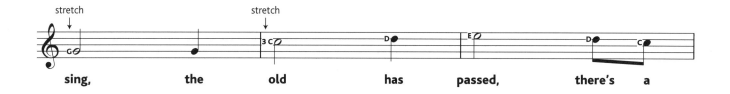

The child is a_____ King, the ca - rol - lers____

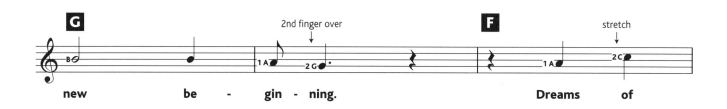

sing, the old has passed, there's a

new be - gin - ning. Dreams of

San - ta, dreams of snow,

fin - gers numb, fa - ces a - glow.

Christ - mas time, mis - tle - toe and

wine, child - ren sing - - ing

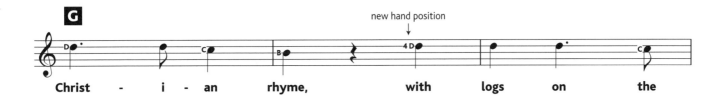

Christ - i - an rhyme, with logs on the

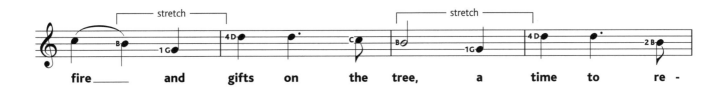

fire___ and gifts on the tree, a time to re -

- joice in the good that we see. see.

Santa Baby

Eartha Kitt

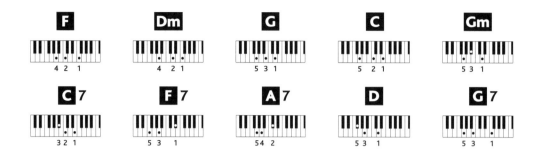

Voice: **Clarinet**
Rhythm: **Swing**
Synchro start: **On**
Tempo: **Moderately** ♩ = 100 (swung quavers)

San - ta ba - by, just slip a sab - le un - der the tree for __ me.

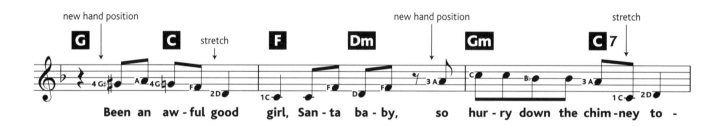

Been an aw - ful good girl, San - ta ba - by, so hur - ry down the chim - ney to -

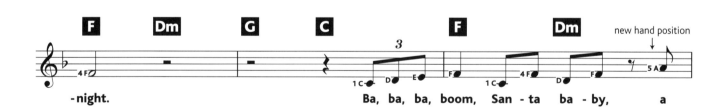

-night. Ba, ba, ba, boom, San - ta ba - by, a

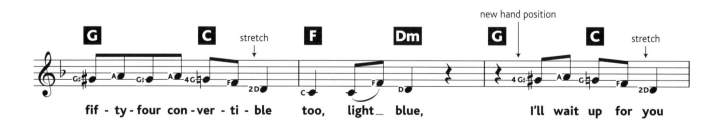

fif - ty - four con - ver - ti - ble too, light __ blue, I'll wait up for you

dear, San - ta ba - by, so hur - ry down the chim - ney to - night.

Think of all the fun I've missed, think of all the fel - las that

I have - n't kissed. __ Next year I could be__ just as good__ if

you check off my Christ - mas list. Ba, ba, ba, boom, San - ta ba - by, I

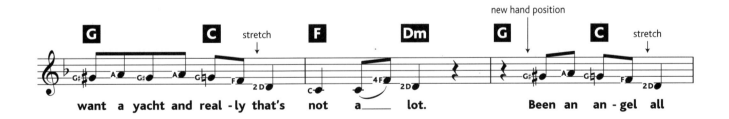

want a yacht and real - ly that's not a__ lot. Been an an - gel all

year, San - ta ba - by, so hur - ry down the chim - ney to - night.

Silent Night

Traditional

Voice: **Piano**
Rhythm: **Waltz**
Synchro start: **On**
Tempo: **Slowly** ♩ = 72

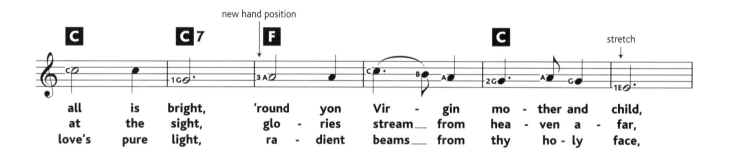

1. Si - lent night, ho - ly night. All is calm,
2. Si - lent night, ho - ly night. Shep - herds quake
3. Si - lent night, ho - ly night. Son of God,

all is bright, 'round yon Vir - gin mo - ther and child,
at the sight, glo - ries stream___ from hea - ven a - far,
love's pure light, ra - dient beams___ from thy ho - ly face,

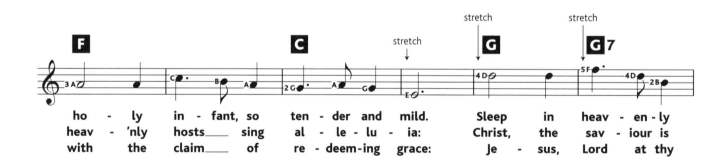

ho - ly in - fant, so ten - der and mild. Sleep in heav - en - ly
heav - 'nly hosts___ sing al - le - lu - ia: Christ, the sav - iour is
with the claim___ of re - deem-ing grace: Je - sus, Lord at thy

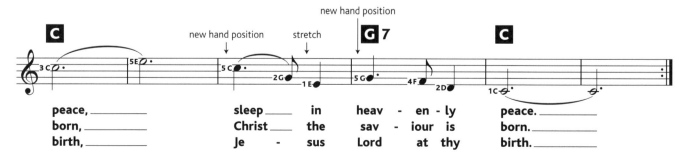

peace,___ sleep___ in heav - en - ly peace.___
born,___ Christ the sav - iour is born.___
birth,___ Je - sus Lord at thy birth.___

Words by Joseph Mohr
Music by Franz Grüber

A Spaceman Came Travelling

Chris de Burgh

Voice: **Flute**
Rhythm: **8th beat**
Synchro start: **On**
Tempo: ♩ = 100

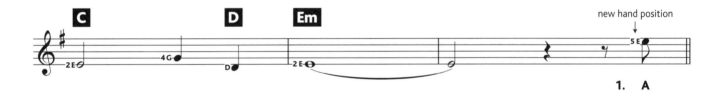

new hand position

1. A

new hand position

space - man	came	trav - 'lling	on	his	ship	from	a - far,	'twas
(2.) fol - lowed	a	light	and	came	down	to	a shed	where a
(3.) stran - ger		spoke,	he	said,	"Do	not	fear.	I

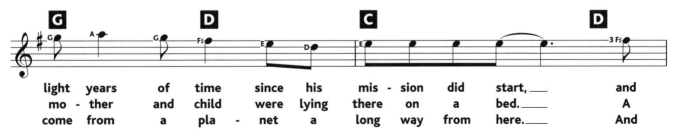

light	years	of	time	since	his	mis - sion	did	start,	and
mo - ther	and	child	were	lying	there	on	a	bed.	A
come	from	a	pla - net	a	long	way	from	here.	And

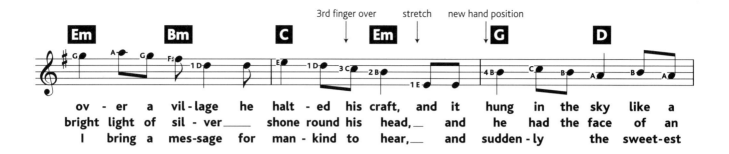

ov - er a vil - lage he halt - ed his craft, and it hung in the sky like a
bright light of sil - ver___ shone round his head,__ and he had the face of an
I bring a mes - sage for man - kind to hear,__ and sudden - ly the sweet-est

star,
angel,   just like a star.___
music   and they were a - fraid.
                                  filled the air.

|1, 2.| |3.|

He   And it went La la la la la la
3. Then the

la la la la   la la la la la la la

la la la la la la la la la la la.   Peace and good - will to all___

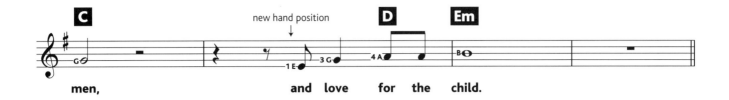

men,   and   love   for   the   child.

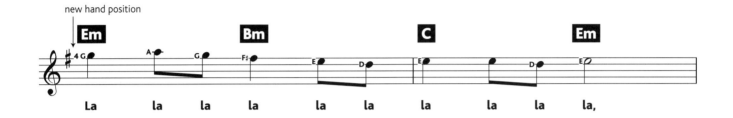

La   la   la   la   la   la   la   la   la   la,

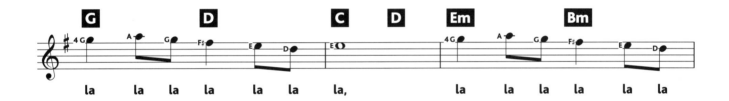

la   la   la   la   la   la   la,   la   la   la   la   la   la

la   la   la   la.   Peace   and   good - will   to   all____ men,

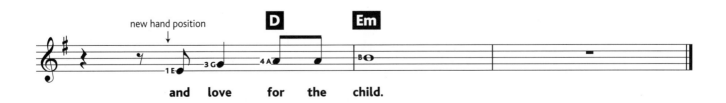

and   love   for   the   child.

Stop The Cavalry

Jona Lewie

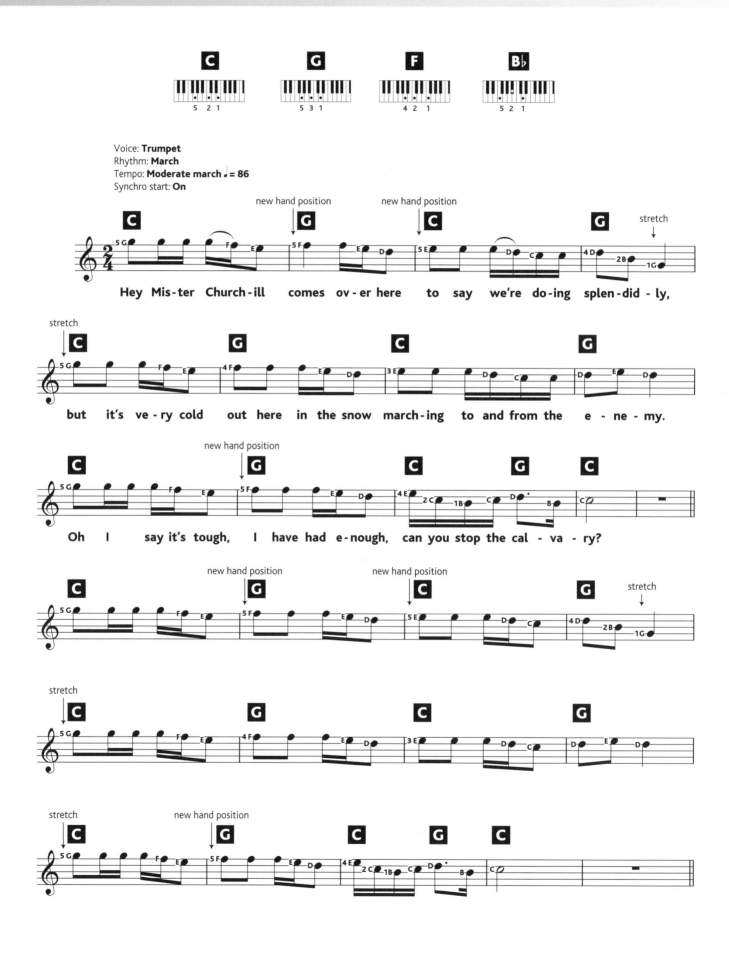

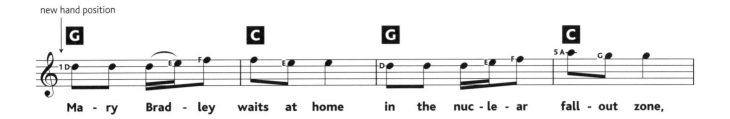

Ma - ry Brad - ley waits at home in the nuc - le - ar fall - out zone,

wish I could be danc - ing now in the arms of the girl I love. _____

Dub a dub a dum dum dub a dub a dum dub a dum dum dub a dub

dub a dub a dum. Dub a dub a dum dum dub a dub a dum dub a

dum dum dub a dub dub a dub a dum. Wish I was at home _____ for

Christ - mas.

We Three Kings Of Orient Are

Traditional

Voice: **Guitar**
Rhythm: **Waltz**
Synchro start: **On**
Tempo: **Not too fast** ♩ = 120

1. We three kings of O - ri - ent
2. Born a king on Beth - le - hem

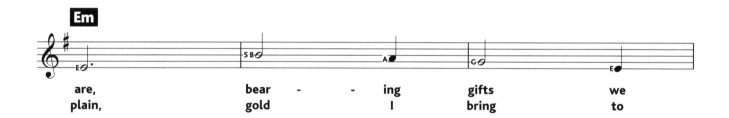

are, bear - ing gifts we
plain, gold I bring we to

tra - verse a - far. Field and
crown him a - gain. King for -

thumb under

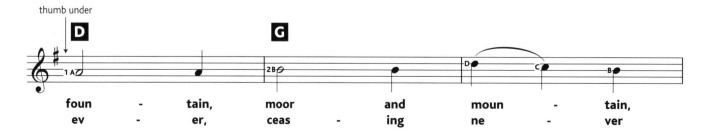

foun - tain, moor and moun - tain,
ev - er, ceas - ing ne - ver

Words & Music by John Henry Hopkins

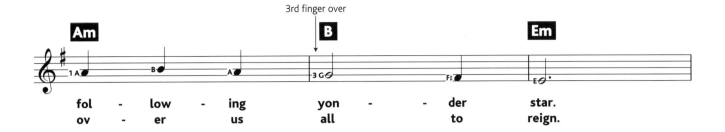

fol - low - ing yon - - der star.
ov - er us all to reign.

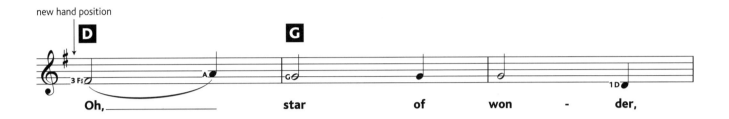

Oh,_____ star of won - der,

star of night, star with

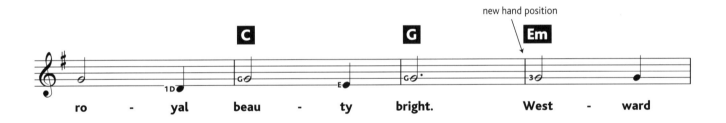

ro - yal beau - ty bright. West - ward

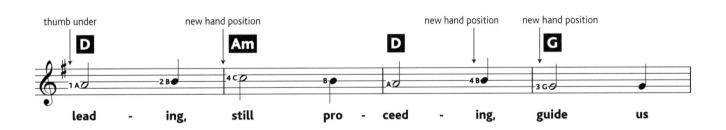

lead - ing, still pro - ceed - ing, guide us

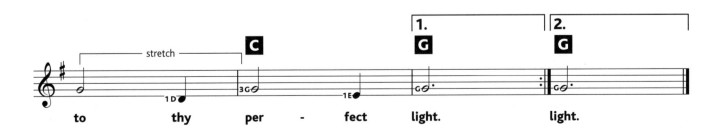

to thy per - fect light. light.

We Wish You A Merry Christmas

Traditional

Voice: **Trumpet**
Rhythm: **Waltz**
Tempo: **Lively** ♩ = 145

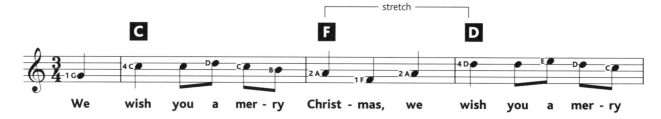

We wish you a mer - ry Christ - mas, we wish you a mer - ry

Christ - mas, we wish you a mer - ry Christ - mas and a

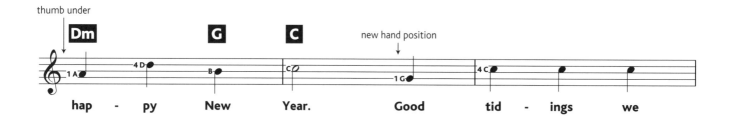

hap - py New Year. Good tid - ings we

bring to you and your kin, we

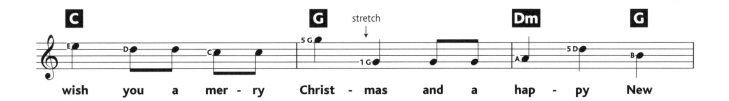

wish you a mer - ry Christ - mas and a hap - py New

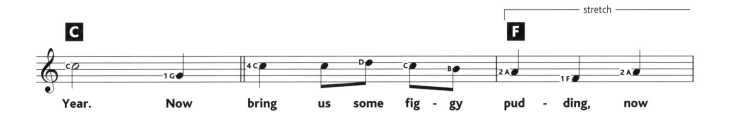

Year. Now bring us some fig - gy pud - ding, now

bring us some fig - gy pud - ding, now bring us some fig - gy

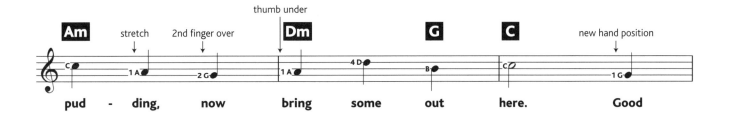

pud - ding, now bring some out here. Good

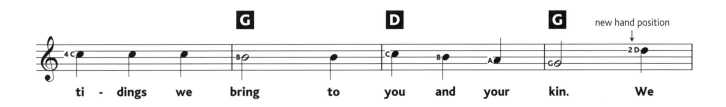

ti - dings we bring to you and your kin. We

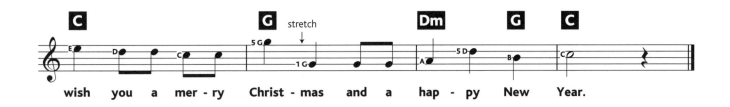

wish you a mer - ry Christ - mas and a hap - py New Year.

Winter Wonderland

Darlene Love

Voice: **Saxophone**
Rhythm: **Swing**
Tempo: **Moderately** ♩ = 96 (swung quavers)

Sleigh bells ring, are you list -'ning? In the lane snow is glist -'ning. A

beau -ti -ful sight, _ we're hap -py to - night, _ walk -ing in a win -ter won -der -

-land. Gone a - way is the blue - bird, here to

stay is a new bird, he sings a love song _ as

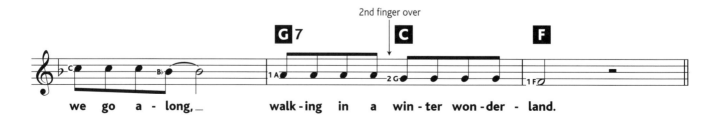

we go a - long, _ walk -ing in a win -ter won -der - land.

Words by Richard Smith
Music by Felix Bernard

In the mea - dow we can build a snow - man, then pre - tend that he is Par - son

Brown. He'll say, "Are you mar - ried?", we'll say, "No, man! But

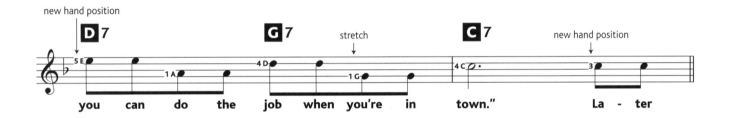

you can do the job when you're in town." La - ter

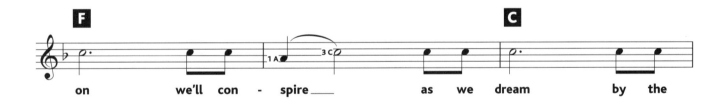

on we'll con - spire____ as we dream by the

fire,____ to face un - a - fraid__ the plans that we made,_

walk - ing in a win - ter won - der - land.

Wonderful Christmastime

Paul McCartney

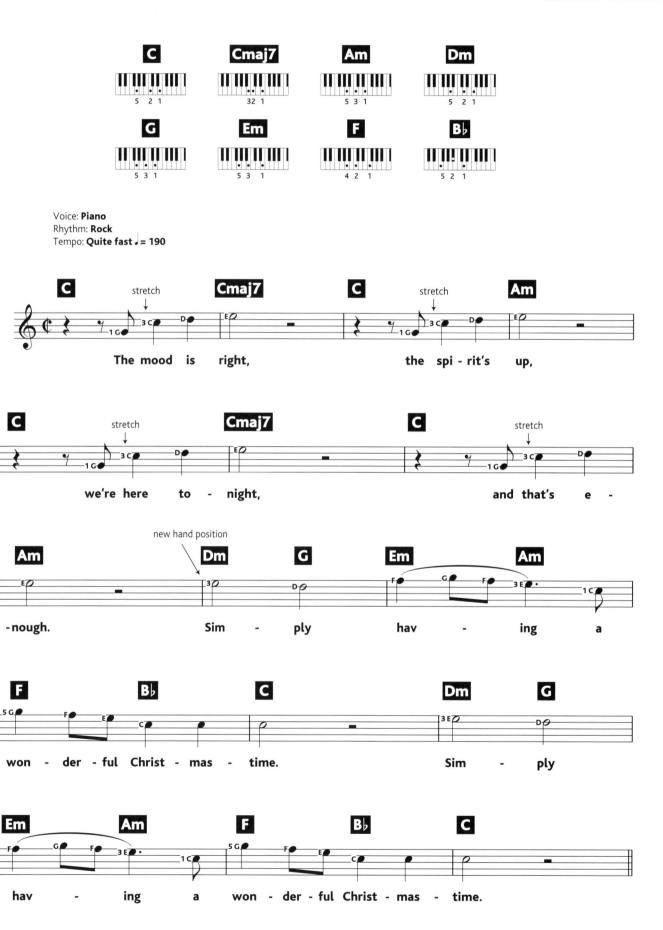

Voice: **Piano**
Rhythm: **Rock**
Tempo: **Quite fast** ♩ = 190

The mood is right, the spi-rit's up,

we're here to-night, and that's e-

-nough. Sim-ply hav-ing a

won-der-ful Christ-mas-time. Sim-ply

hav-ing a won-der-ful Christ-mas-time.

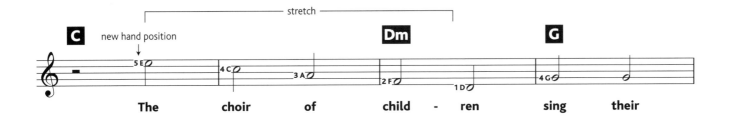

The   choir   of   child - ren   sing   their

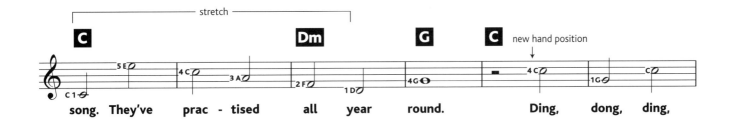

song. They've   prac - tised   all   year   round.   Ding,   dong,   ding,

dong,   ding,   dong,   ding.   Ooh,

___ ooh.

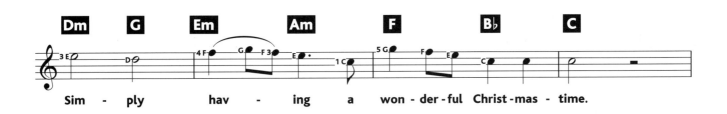

Sim - ply   hav - ing   a   won - der - ful Christ - mas - time.

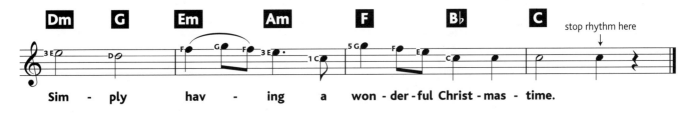

Sim - ply   hav - ing   a   won - der - ful Christ - mas - time.

Bringing you the words and the music

All the latest music in print... rock & pop plus jazz, blues, country, classical and the best in West End show scores.

- Books to match your favourite CDs.

- Book-and-CD titles with high quality backing tracks for you to play along to. Now you can play guitar or piano with your favourite artist... or simply sing along!

- Audition songbooks with CD backing tracks for both male and female singers for all those with stars in their eyes.

- Can't read music? No problem, you can still play all the hits with our wide range of chord songbooks.

- Check out our range of instrumental tutorial titles, taking you from novice to expert in no time at all!

- Musical show scores include *The Phantom Of The Opera*, *Les Misérables*, *Mamma Mia* and many more hit productions.

- DVD master classes featuring the techniques of top artists.